A
BEACHCOMBER'S
BOTANY

A
BEACHCOMBER'S
BOTANY

Essays and Comments by
LOREN C. PETRY

Illustrations and Captions by
MARCIA G. NORMAN

Published by

THE
CHATHAM CONSERVATION FOUNDATION,
INC.

Chatham, Massachusetts

PREFACE

T<small>HIS</small> <small>IS</small> a book about Cape Cod shores and the plants that grow there. Its illustrations will be useful as far west as Long Island and as far north as Cape Breton.

All proceeds from its sale go to The Chatham Conservation Foundation, Inc., an organization in Chatham, Massachusetts which is dedicated to preserving valuable and irreplaceable marshes, beaches, and uplands.

A growing number of other organizations in the United States have the same aim. In helping one, you help all, for as recognition of the importance of conserving our natural resources in one area increases, the knowledge spreads to benefit others.

Not all who visit our seashores know the plants they see there, or the importance of the sand flats and the salt marshes to the wild life they support. This book is designed to give information on such matters and, in this way, to make new friends for conservation.

Loren C. Petry
Marcia G. Norman
April, 1968

ACKNOWLEDGMENTS

THE AUTHORS wish to express their grateful appreciation to the following individuals who have assisted in the preparation of this book:

EDWARD WEEKS, of The Atlantic Monthly, for permission to quote from his article on salt marshes;

RICHARD J. EATON, Curator of Vascular Plants, New England Botanical Club Herbarium, for his expert help, and for advice on the selection of material;

GEORGE H. M. LAWRENCE, Director, Rachel M. M. Hunt Botanical Library, Pittsburgh, for information about introduced plants;

ROBERT A. TAYLOR, Park Naturalist, Cape Cod National Seashore, for his assistance in the field;

RICHARD P. KORF, of the Plant Pathology Herbarium of Cornell University, for validation of the scientific names of some fungi;

W. STEPHEN THOMAS, Director of the Rochester Museum of Arts and Sciences, for aid in the selection of books and reference material; and to

WALTER J. SHEA, President Emeritus of the Boston Mycological Club, for information about the structure and identification of the rare mushroom from Monomoy.

CONTENTS

THE SHORE AND THE BEACH

THE SHORE borders the sea or the lake, makes the transition from land to water, and confronts the solid, unmoving earth with the constant movement of wave or tide. This is the most familiar of the three great confrontations of nature, and the most obvious. Both members of the confronting pair are visible to us; one is always quiet, and the other is never quiet. Only in the thunderstorm on the prairie or the hurricane at sea do we recognize the spectacular character that the confrontation of land and air, or of water and air, may assume; but the turmoil of the waves of a northeaster on the Cape Cod shore is familiar.

The beach, that part of the shore where its two components constantly overlap, is the essential feature of the shore, and the center of our attention. Its width depends in part on its steepness. The great beach of the Atlantic shore of Cape Cod is relatively steep and narrow; compare it with the beaches of New Jersey, of Florida, or of Cornwall. High tides and vigorous wave action in general produce wide beaches. The Great Lakes, without appreciable tides and usually with only moderate wave action, have narrow beaches. The Bras D'Or of Cape Breton, with tides measured in inches and only moderate waves in the highest of winds, has only narrow beaches or none. The Bay of Fundy is famous for its tremendous tides, but on its steep and rocky shores only beaches of moderate width occur.

Obviously it is on the beaches that we can expect to find samples of the plants and animals of the adjacent waters, sea or bay or lake. *Sargassum* and other free-floating seaweeds, unattached molluscs such as the whelks and scallops, accumulate at the landward margin of the beach.

And after a storm attached forms such as *Fucus* and *Alaria* also appear there, broken loose from their anchorages by the underwater violence of the waves and carried up by the heightened tide. And because the plants and animals of the lake or sea are so different from those of the land, and unfamiliar to most of us, every visitor to the shore turns beachcomber and hopefully searches the windrow of debris at the high tide line for something rare or at least unusual.

It is on the slope just above high tide line, that part of the beach for which we have no special name, and on the ridge of windblown sand behind it, that we find the herbaceous flowering plants typical of the shore. Here we find beach grass, beach pea, dusty miller, cocklebur, sandwort, and all the others illustrated and named in the drawings that follow.

Still further back from the beach, where the wind-blown sand has not been abundant enough to bury their bases, are the shrubs and vines of a sandy coast: poison ivy and its shrubby relatives, the sumacs; bayberry, wild roses, and beach plum. These, too, are best learned from the illustrations and the captions accompanying them. Behind and often over these are the trees; pitch pine and oaks for the most part. These have two characteristics that have enabled them to survive on our coasts; they regenerate themselves after fire, and they are not destroyed by salt spray and the violence of hurricane winds.

But it must be noted that not all shores have beaches. Shores without beaches are those which show one or the other of two extreme conditions: they are either precipitous or they are very flat. Where cliffs descend directly into the water, and to some depth below, no beach can form until wave erosion has cut a bench to hold it. On the other hand, in small coves with narrow mouths, and in estuaries whose openings are sheltered by sand bars, land and sea frequently meet in salt marsh. These salt marshes, with no sand visible except in the creeks, and with no water over most of the area except at the time of high-course or spring tides, are the exact functional equivalent of our beaches on other parts of our shores; and these salt marshes bear the most compact plant growth of all our shores.

Cape Cod, Martha's Vineyard, and Nantucket are glacial in origin, and as a result are largely composed of sand and gravel. They lie at the eastern margin of the North American continent, in the middle latitudes (41° − 42° N), and therefore have a temperate climate considerably modified by their marine environment. These factors − sandy soil, temperate climate, and marine environment − largely determine the composition of the vegetation of our shores. Because of its importance in this regard, this marine environment is discussed in some detail in the following chapter.

OCEAN, BAY, AND SOUND

THE NORTH ATLANTIC coast, from the mouth of the Hudson River to the northern tip of Newfoundland, is a fascinating area, and all its aspects have been duly described by many skilled writers. The Appalachian folding which began nearly 400 million years ago not only established the sweeping curve of the Gulf of Maine, the Gaspé Peninsula, and the mainland of Nova Scotia, but also laid down the underwater foundation on which Long Island, Block Island, Martha's Vineyard, Nantucket, and Cape Cod were later built. And in all this area the same general arrangement of land and water prevails. Peninsulas and islands lie more or less parallel to the mainland, separated from it by relatively narrow and quiet gulfs, bays, sounds, or estuaries, and exposed on the other side to the open and often stormy ocean. Just where a particular bit of shore lies in this general arrangement determines its character and often what plants we will find on it.

Long Island, the Vineyard, Nantucket, and Cape Cod are almost entirely the product of the great ice sheets which once lay over this part of North America and which disappeared a mere 10,000 years ago. Only in the western part of Long Island and about Gay Head on Martha's Vineyard do any materials of non-glacial origin appear at or above sea level. All the Cape is made up of glacial debris — clay, silt, sand, gravel, small and large boulders, and a few huge boulders, with no cemented bedrock anywhere at its surface. Ever since the last ice sheet melted away, three substantially different bodies of water have been battering the shores of this relatively uniform mass of unconsolidated materials. These bodies of water are, of course, the Atlantic Ocean, Cape Cod Bay, and Nantucket Sound.

There are significant differences in the characteristics and behavior of these three bodies of water. These differences are of course not chemical in character, except for some small differences in salinity. But that there are differences in temperature any bather will testify. The Ocean water is coldest, almost as cold as that of Casco Bay. The water of the Bay is warmer, but not as warm as that of the Sound; only the shallow fresh-water ponds are warmer than the Sound. The mean range of the tide on the Ocean side is about six and a half feet; on the Bay side, from nine to ten feet; and on the Sound side, from two to four feet. There is also a difference in the frequency of the waves — a difference easy to demonstrate by timing them on the three shores at places where the approach of the waves is not hampered by bars or projecting points of land.

The Ocean shore is being rapidly eroded. The average rate is about three feet a year, but the maximum is almost twice this. As a result of this erosion, the banks back of the beach are constantly crumbling and sliding, and it is unusual to see any plants growing on these. On this shore, then, we will find our plants on the sand ridges and dunes above and behind these slopes, and among the debris cast up by high tides and storm waves.

The Sound shore nowhere shows such pronounced erosion, and deposition is occurring at some places. The beaches are much wider in proportion to the tide rise than those of the Ocean shore, and they have a gentler slope. The Sound is shallow, and a southwest storm throws up a wealth of plant and animal material. There are no true dunes on the Sound shore, but the sand ridges carry the dune plants. Salt marshes in the estuaries are usual, but the forest does not come as close to the beach as on the Bay side.

Because of the great mean tide range, the Bay beaches are relatively wide. In Brewster and Orleans a sandy tidal flat is exposed at each neap tide and it is then possible to walk with very little wading over several square miles of the temporarily exposed Bay floor. Rocks, boulders, and gravel, left behind as the finer material of the glacial debris is washed away, are common all along the south shore of the Bay. Sometimes an apron of large rocks is exposed in this way. These break the waves and protect the shore behind them from much of the erosion that would otherwise occur, and a projecting point of land results. Nobscusset Point in Dennis and Point of Rocks in Brewster are examples.

The estuaries of the Bay shore all contain salt marshes. Some of these marshes surround higher land with typical upland vegetation; pine and oak forest and associated plants. These higher areas are called islands, even though they are surrounded by water only a few times each month; Wing's Island in Brewster is the most striking example of this. In Yarmouth and Dennis a continuous salt marsh of 600 acres surrounds Bass Hole at the mouth of Chase Garden Creek; in the west end of Barnstable Harbor there is a continuous salt marsh of even greater extent.

The collector of shells will find significant differences between those found in the Bay and those in the Sound. Whelk shells are common on Sound beaches; one found on a Bay beach has probably been carried there and discarded. Razor clams are abundant on the Bay beaches of Eastham; rare on Sound beaches. Most of the common seaweeds are found on all the beaches, but *Sargassum* is an exception; it is common in the Sound, rare on Ocean beaches, absent from the Bay.

HOW PLANTS ARE NAMED

Wʜᴇɴ ʏᴏᴜ are shown an unfamiliar object, you ask, "What is it?" For an answer you expect a name, not an explanation. Since objects are frequently bulky, or inconvenient to handle, or difficult to preserve, we keep the name instead of the object, accompanying it with enough remembered details to distinguish it from another object with different remembered details. As this process continues, we gradually acquire a list of names which are for many purposes just as satisfactory as the objects themselves.

Of course names will not serve for every purpose. If you want to know how long an object is, only a picture drawn to scale, or a detailed description, or the object itself, will serve. On the other hand, when manipulation or arrangement is required, the names are more satisfactory than the objects themselves. We have all at some time been taught a new card game. Consider what the problem of learning would have been if your instructor had only shown you the cards, but had never given you names for them.

How the naming of plants and animals began does not concern us here, but how it developed its present practice does. Until a few hundreds of years ago, physicians were the principal practicing botanists, for it was from plants that they derived most of their remedies. Dioscorides, a Greek physician, in 78 A. D. published the first extensive list of plants of the eastern Mediterranean, a list so useful that it was referred to by physicians and botanists for the next 1500 years.

In these earlier lists short descriptions served as names. Illustrations assisted by indicating the essential features of particular plants, and the

18

figures of the 15th and 16th century herbals were both accurate and beautiful. By 1750 biologists were ready for the innovation of using two words, the second as a modifier of the first, to name an organism, and at the same time to indicate something of its relationship to other similar organisms. This binomial system, with which the name of Carolus Linnaeus is always associated, has been adopted by biologists all over the world. An international organization which meets at intervals and operates by committees between meetings, has formulated rules for the validation of names already published, and, as needed, interprets the rules. When the discoverer of a new plant publishes a technical description of it, he proposes a name for it. If the proposed name is in accord with the rules — has not been previously used for some other organism, for example — it is accepted and becomes the only valid name for the plant.

These names are the scientific names used in all technical publications. Each consists of a *generic* name (name of a genus), followed by a *specific* name (name of a species), followed by the name (or abbreviation of the name) of the describer. Thus the name of our common beach plum is *Prunus maritima* Marsh. This indicates that the botanist Humphrey Marshall first published a technical description of this plant. He recognized that it is similar to, and related to, other plums, and so should be given the generic name *Prunus;* and he suggested the name *maritima* as a specific name. This was all in accordance with the rules, and *Prunus maritima* Marsh. is the name to be applied to this plant wherever it grows. Because it is not essential to know the name of the describer in most cases, that is usually omitted except in technical articles.

But many plants and animals, the common ones certainly, have common or colloquial names, and for most purposes these are to be preferred to the scientific names whenever they will serve. Unfortunately, a common name used in one locality for one particular plant may be used elsewhere for a very different plant. *Nyssa sylvatica* is a handsome tree of the eastern United States, with branches which extend out from the trunk almost horizontally, and with simple leaves which turn magnificently red in a good autumn. Throughout most of its range, from central Maine to Florida, it is called sour gum, black gum, pepperidge, or tupelo; any one of these names will be recognized as referring to this tree. But in eastern Massachusetts, and especially on Cape Cod and the Islands, and apparently nowhere else, this tree is called hornbeam.

To add to the confusion, several plants may have the same common name. For example, there are four poverty grasses and five pigweeds in New England. And then there are many where the common name gives incorrect information about a plant. For example, black grass (*Juncus Gerardi*) is a rush, not a grass, and most bulrushes are not rushes but sedges. To have the convenience of using the familiar common names without the uncertainties suggested above, it is general practice to give the accepted scientific name when a common name is first used, and then to use that common name only as a synonym for that scientific name. This is the practice followed throughout this book.

It should also be noted that lists of scientific names are not fixed, and that changes have to be made from time to time. Species new to an area may be introduced intentionally or accidentally. Competent investigators may report evidence to warrant the reclassification of a form or variety as a species. It is therefore customary to select some recent authoritative list, and to use the scientific names given and defined there. Throughout this book the scientific names given in Gray's *Manual of Botany,* Eighth Edition, M. L. Fernald, Editor, have been used.

AT THE TIDE LINE

THE RAGGED band of debris at the high tide line gives us abundant samples of the vegetation down to low tide and well below. The ridge of water on which the surf-boarder rides has its counterpart in equally violent motion beneath the surface, and in a storm this tears loose whatever grows there. Picked up fresh, these plants from the sea (with one exception to be described later) show some characteristics common to all. All are soft and pliable; none is woody. The shapes are relatively simple; they often branch, but they never have roots, stems, or leaves. Attached forms have been fastened to rocks or shells by simple "holdfasts." They are all simple in structure; none consists of more than a few kinds of cells. All depend on water to support them; none could support itself in the air. Walk out on the Brewster or Orleans flats at low tide and note how these plants drape themselves over the rocks to which they are attached.

In size these plants range from a few cells visible with the microscope to an occasional kelp 10 or 15 feet in length. Here we can deal only with the larger forms. The collector finds the dried specimens disappointing and usually discards them. Teachers who want to display the brown ones in a more satisfactory form can put fresh specimens in jars and cover them with glycerine. This shrinks them and destroys some of the color, but preserves them in satisfactory condition. When the specimens are transferred from the glycerine to water they regain their size, their slimy feel, and their salt-flat odor! The red ones can be floated out on heavy paper and dried in a warm oven without losing their color; with luck and skill attractive preparations can be made in this way.

21

These plants, cast up by wave and tide, and commonly called seaweeds, are technically known as marine algae. On the basis of structure, reproductive methods, and the pigments they display, they are classified as green, brown, and red algae. We commonly find only three green algae on our beaches, and for only one of these, *Ulva lactuca,* do we have a satisfactory common name, sea lettuce. The others are *Enteromorpha* and *Codium.* These possess the same pigments as our higher plants, and so are leaf green in color. Sea lettuce and *Enteromorpha* are small and delicate in structure, but *Codium* is larger and sturdier. It is a relative newcomer to our shores, having been accidentally brought with "seed oysters" from Chesapeake Bay. It may prove to be a pest, since it detrimentally affects the growth of any shellfish to which it attaches itself. It seriously interferes with the movements of scallops, and in onshore storms causes them to be dragged into shallow water or onto the beach.

The brown algae vary in color from yellow brown to olive brown. They possess the same green pigments that the green algae do, but the abundant brown pigments hide them, and it requires a simple chemical manipulation to demonstrate their occurrence. If chopped or crushed material of a living brown alga is put in a vial with methanol (wood alcohol) or with the denatured alcohol the druggist can sell you, a brown solution results in a few hours. If this solution is now poured into a clean vial, a few drops of kerosene added, and the mixture shaken, the two materials will soon separate; the kerosene, floating on the alcohol, will be distinctly green. In this experiment, the alcohol has been used to dissolve all the pigments in the wet tissues of the alga. The green pigments are more readily soluble in the kerosene than in the alcohol, and appear in it when the two separate after mixing.

The red algae are mostly smaller and more delicate than the brown algae. They prefer warmer waters and are more abundant in the Sound than in the other waters. The green pigments are present in these as in the other marine algae, and can be demonstrated in the same way. Irish moss, *Chondrus crispus,* is common on our beaches. It is an article of commerce to furnish a gelatine-like material used in ice cream and in other foods, and is regularly harvested on Nova Scotia shores; but it is not abundant enough on the Cape to warrant commercial collecting.

Mixed in with the seaweeds, and frequently more abundant than all of them together we find the exception previously mentioned, eelgrass, *Zostera marina,* variety *stenophylla.* This is a flowering plant, with creeping underground stems, roots at the nodes, and ribbon-like leaves less than a quarter of an inch in width but two or three feet in length. When washed ashore the leaves quickly blacken, but a little search will usually produce some basal leaves still attached to the stem. Examination of these with a hand lens will show three parallel veins running the length of the leaf, and abundant transverse veinlets.

Eelgrass is related to some of our fresh-water pond weeds, but it grows only in salt water, and only below high tide line. Along the North Atlantic shore it was attacked by a virus disease in the 1940s and was largely killed out, but it is now thriving again here. It is well to remember that there is another eelgrass, *Vallisneria spiralis,* on the Cape, growing only in fresh water, and different from *Zostera* in almost every way except that it, too, has long narrow underwater leaves.

THE TYPICAL SHORE PLANTS

THE PLANTS that we always expect to find on our shores, those that give the characteristic background to our beaches, are all flowering plants, and all herbaceous. Most of them are perennials; a few are annuals. As already mentioned, they inhabit the slope just above the usual high tide line and the ridge of wind-blown sand behind it. A few of these plants have already been mentioned, and many more are illustrated and named in the following pages, but some deserve further description.

On the sand ridges behind the beaches, and on the fixed parts of our dunes, and anywhere else that wind-blown sand has accumulated within reach of salt spray, we find beach grass, *Ammophila breviligulata*. It is the one of our local grasses that can be identified by the leaf alone, for the upper side — the side toward the stem — shows ten or twelve parallel lines running from base to tip of the blade. A hand lens will show that these lines are ridges alternating with grooves; each contains a vein. This ribbed structure causes the leaves of beach grass to roll up more or less tightly whenever the water supply of the plant is deficient, and to unroll promptly when more water becomes available. This adaptation occurs in many grasses, but beach grass is the only one of our shore grasses that possesses it.

A little judicious digging will show how beach grass spreads, by the growth, at the depth of only a few inches, of the horizontal underground stems called rhizomes. These are the principal stems of the grass, with enlarged nodes separated by internodes a few inches in length. At each node fibrous roots grow out into the sand, and absorb from it the water and dissolved minerals necessary for the growth of the plant. At the tip of the rhizome is the bud whose periodic growth has produced it.

At intervals, at every fifth to tenth node, a lateral bud develops on the upper side of the rhizome and grows upward until it reaches the surface of the sand. This bud then produces a short erect stem, with some roots about its base. The erect stem, which presently branches, produces a cluster of the long, ribbed leaves already described. This is the beach grass plant we see; the rhizome is hidden in the ground. After a year or two the main bud produces an inflorescence, flowers, fruits, and seeds, and then dies. In the meantime, other erect branches have developed, and our plant is apparently a cluster of plants, any one of which may produce an inflorescence, and then die.

How long do beach grass plants live? Do some digging and make your own estimate. Do new plants ever develop from seeds? Yes, but seedling plants are rare. In places where it is desirable to check the blowing of sand in a dune area, beach grass is often planted. For this purpose, rhizomes are dug up, cut into pieces, each with an aboveground stem, and the pieces are planted at suitable intervals. A good stand of the grass is quickly obtained in this way. The beach grass growing about the Marconi Wireless Station site in the Cape Cod National Seashore in South Wellfleet was all planted only a few years ago.

Most of the perennials of the sand ridges display the same vegetative behavior as the beach grass. They have prostrate creeping stems, which root and branch at intervals, and send up erect stems which bear the flowers, fruits, and seeds. Beach pea, *Lathyrus japonicus,* variety *glaber,* and dusty miller, *Artemisia Stelleriana,* are familiar examples. In both of these the creeping stems are at the surface of the ground, not below it.

Cakile edentula, sea rocket, and *Xanthium echinatum,* cocklebur, are annuals of this habitat. Their seeds germinate early enough, and their seedlings grow fast enough, to produce mature plants, flowers, fruits, and seeds in a single season. The bur of the cocklebur is the fruit, with two elongated seeds side by side enclosed within. Because of slight differences in the seed coats of the two seeds, one usually germinates the next season, the other a year or two later. This behavior gives a surprise to anyone attempting to eradicate cocklebur from a field or garden. Other plants of this habitat, annuals, a few biennials, and many perennials, can be easily recognized by comparison with the illustrations in this book.

The woody plants of our shores — vines, shrubs, and trees — will be discussed when we consider the conditions at the transition zone from a salt marsh to the upland on which these woody plants grow. And before discussing the salt marshes, the largest in area of all our habitats, it is necessary to discuss grasses, the principal component of the marshes, and some of their relatives, the sedges and rushes. Without such a preliminary explanation, the user of this book will find it difficult to distinguish members of the three groups, especially since the common names are often not helpful, and sometimes may be positively confusing.

GRASSES, RUSHES, AND SEDGES

No MATTER where we live or what we do, we are familiar with grasses —
in the lawns we mow, the pastures by which we drive, or the prairies we
fly over. The grasses are the most abundant of all the flowering plants
and, in terms of their value to man, by far the most important. Consider
the problem of food supply for man and beast if we had no wheat, no
rice, no oats, no corn, no pasture grasses; or read the science fiction thriller
Death of Grass, by John Christopher. Of the 6,000 species of grasses
described for the entire world, nearly 500 are found in central and northeastern United States and eastern Canada, and more than half of these
occur in New England.

In general, grasses are herbaceous and small; the bamboos, corn, and
reed, Phragmites, are not typical grasses. Grass stems are cylindrical and
enlarged at the nodes, the places where the leaves are attached. The nodes
are always solid, but the internodes may be either hollow or solid. The
leaves are alternate in attachment. The leaf has two principal parts; the
sheath, attached to the stem all the way around the node and clasping the
stem, but open at the side opposite the blade; and the blade, long, narrow,
parallel-veined, and usually flat, and extending away from the stem at an
angle.

The flowers of the grasses are small, and have no sepals or petals
recognizable as such. They are enclosed in bracts and always arranged in
clusters of various kinds. The fruit, when ripe, is a grain which never
opens to discharge the single seed it contains. Instead, the fruit (grain)
functions as a seed, is distributed as a seed would be, and produces a young
plant as a seed would do. It is in fact a seed with an extra protective layer,
the fruit wall or pericarp.

26

The rushes are similar in aspect to the grasses and often occur in the same habitats; one genus, *Luzula,* often occurs in lawns. They are much less common than grasses and sedges — only two genera occur in New England — but they may be dominant plants in small areas. The stems are cylindrical in form, with the nodes not much enlarged, and solid throughout. The leaves may be in basal clusters, or few on an erect stem, or entirely absent; in the latter case the green stem carries on the process of photosynthesis. On an erect stem the leaves have a clasping sheath, open at least a part of the way down, and a blade either flat and grass-like, or cylindrical and needle-like.

The rushes are readily distinguished from the grasses by their flowers and fruits. The flowers have three sepals and three petals; these are small, green or brown in color, and persistent, not falling off when the fruit matures. The fruit is also persistent, and when it is mature it splits into three valves, thus releasing the seeds. All these features can be readily distinguished with a hand lens, or in many cases with the naked eye.

The sedges are similar to the grasses and rushes in general appearance, but differ from them in several ways. The stem is usually solid and triangular in cross section, but the angles may be rounded enough to give the impression of a cylindrical form. The leaves are sometimes clustered at the base or just below a flower cluster at the tip of the stem. It is then difficult to determine the leaf arrangement; but when they are arranged along the stem it is easy to see that they are in three ranks. Each leaf consists of a tubular sheath, not open at the side, and a long, narrow, flat blade.

The flowers of the sedges are roughly like those of the grasses, without sepals and petals, and in clusters. The fruits do not open to discharge the seeds. In favorable habitats the sedges are abundant, but they seldom take over the ground as the grasses do.

We can sort out the grasses by the cylindrical stem, two ranks of leaves, and open leaf sheath, and can check by the absence of sepals, petals, and open fruits. The triangular stem, three ranks of leaves, and closed (tubular) leaf sheath indicate the sedges, with a check by flower and fruit characters. The flower and fruit characters identify the rushes.

There are a few large grasses that are sure to attract attention and to produce a demand for names. Most conspicuous of all is the reed, *Phragmites communis,* variety *Berlandieri.* Fresh water and brackish water are both acceptable to it, and you will find it in both habitats here. The species, with its varieties, is widely distributed in temperate and warmer climates, but it may be a newcomer to the Cape, for it has not yet monopolized the suitable habitats, as it has on Long Island, for example.

The reed always grows in pure stands, with nothing else mixed in. The characteristic dense clusters are produced by rapid vegetative propagation by horizontally growing rhizomes. It is always as tall as a man, and colonies twice as tall are not unusual. The individual stems of any colony, nearly uniform in height and therefore producing a flat-topped mass, are terminated in late summer by handsome much-branched feathery plumes, the inflorescences in which the flowers are produced. The reed is apparently self-sterile and rarely produces viable seeds. The inflorescences when mature vary in color from gray to almost black; but those of any colony will all be of one color. These differences in color are not indicators of varieties, but only of color forms. Even the most casual observer cannot miss these great colonies, ranging in size from a few square yards to an acre or more, each with a level roof of handsome nodding plumes.

Two *Spartinas* larger than the salt marsh pioneer, *Spartina alterniflora,* are found in a few places on the Cape. The first of these, salt reedgrass, *Spartina cynosuroides,* grows to a height of five feet or a little more. It occurs as single plants loosely scattered at the upper level at which salt marsh grass will grow, and because of its size, becomes a striking element in those salt marshes in which it is found. Its bottle-brush inflorescence and its size distinguish it from all the other salt marsh grasses. It occurs in the upper Cape, in Brewster, and in Wellfleet; reports of its occurrence elsewhere on the Cape would be welcomed.

Similar in size but of different habitat is *Spartina pectinata,* fresh-water cord-grass. As its common name indicates, it does not usually occur in salt water. You may expect to find it in the upper parts of those estuaries that hold salt marshes further down, and it sometimes occurs in abandoned cranberry bogs. Its inflorescence is unsymmetrical and easily recognized.

Most of the other important grasses of the shore, and one important rush, *Juncus Gerardi,* grow in and about the salt marshes, and can best be discussed in that connection. As for the sedges, learn to distinguish them from the grasses at sight, and do not be confused by the fact that several of them are called "bulrushes."

THE SALT MARSH

Every interested visitor to our shores should walk out onto a salt marsh at low tide; should note the lines of taller grass that mark the courses of the creeks; should note the differences of color that mark the areas of the various shorter grasses; and should note the zonation of the vegetation around its margin. He should visit the same marsh a week later, arriving about an hour before a high-course tide reaches its crest; should watch the tide sweep over the marsh, submerging all but the tall grass along the creeks; should watch the tide recede and the water drain off; and should note which of the shorter grasses emerge first, which last.

He should then engage a pilot to take him for a flight over the same marsh; should note the unexpectedly tortuous courses of the creeks; and should note the numerous water-filled pools scattered about the marsh, and drained only by artificial ditches in the interest of mosquito control. He should then return to the marsh at low tide, equipped with a strong, sharp spade; should dig into the surface with his spade, to get a sample of the peat he has been walking upon; should get another sample at the edge of a creek, where the taller grasses grow; should take his samples home, wash the mud out, and examine and compare their structure and texture.

He should return again at low tide, equipped with a long sharp-pointed rod; should thrust the rod down until it strikes the gravel underlying the peat; should repeat at intervals, recording the depths at each sounding; and should compute, in thousands of cubic feet, the volume of the peat in the marsh. When he has done these things, he is ready to examine the plants which not only grow in the marsh, but have by their growth produced the marsh.

The taller grass along the creeks is salt marsh grass, also called cord-grass, *Spartina alterniflora*. This is the pioneer in salt marsh formation. It grows on slopes such as creek banks down to about half tide level; that is, the bases of these plants are submerged for about half the time. You can see it invading the sand flats of Brewster, Orleans, and Eastham, growing out into the Bay with only the tips of its leaves showing at high tide. In an established salt marsh the conditions for its growth occur only in the lower areas, and especially along the creeks. The larger creeks are too deep for salt-marsh grass to grow on their bottoms, and so they are never blocked by it; and the surge of the tide in and out helps to keep these creeks open.

Salt marsh grass grows up to four feet in height, but it cannot be identified by height alone. When it is very crowded it will sometimes produce fully developed inflorescences and flowers at a third of that height. Once established as a seedling, its propagation is vegetative, by underground rhizomes. Here again the sand flats give us the best illustrative material and, at low tide, ideal conditions for investigation.

When the level of the salt marsh has been built up to about high tide level, other grasses take over, displacing the salt marsh grass. These new grasses are the ones which were once cut for hay and fed to domestic animals, and the marshes at this level were often called salt meadows. Two new grasses and a rush now dominate the marsh; these are high-water grass, *Spartina patens;* spike grass, *Distichlis spicata;* and a rush, *Juncus Gerardi,* with the accepted common name of black grass. These are all of moderate height, 13 to 15 inches. They do not grow scattered about, like dandelions in your lawn, but in almost pure stands, one kind in each area, high water grass here, black grass there, spike grass yonder.

Slight differences in elevation or drainage are sufficient to determine which one occupies a particular spot. Once established, they maintain themselves by their very effective vegetative propagation.

In general, spike grass favors the wetter places — not as wet as those where salt marsh grass holds the ground, but only a few inches higher. Its leaves are flat and light green in color. At full low tide you can look over a marsh and say with some certainty that in that light green patch you will get your feet wet.

The high water grass is suitably named, since it occupies the average level of the marsh. Its branching spikes of a purplish color and its dark green leaves mark it from a distance. A specimen in hand shows a character which will serve to identify it when it is not in flower. The leaf is not flat, like that of spike grass, but folded upward, so that a cross section is U-shaped, with the open side of the U up.

The third member of the association, the black grass, grows at the highest level of the three. Here it is regularly flooded at each high-course tide, but only for a very short time. In mass it is very dark in color, because of the black fruits which ripen as early as June and persist into the autumn.

The typical salt meadow is half or more occupied by high water grass; half or less by spike grass and black grass together. Scattered through this assemblage, but most abundant in the wetter parts where some salt marsh grass still lingers, are those other plants we always associate with salt marshes, even though they are never very abundant anywhere. No mature salt marsh is without its delicately branched sea lavender in scattered clumps; nor without the glassworts so inconspicuous in summer, and so striking in their flaming red in an occasional December.

Around the borders at first, but soon pressing in toward the wetter parts, seaside goldenrod makes its appearance in August and persists into the autumn, to give way at last to the tawny color of our marsh grasses that is the glory of our winter seashore. In the higher places along the creeks one or two species of bulrushes can usually be found, with the triangular stems that warn you that in spite of their common names they are sedges, not rushes.

For the hunter of semi-rarities who will refrain from lavish collecting, there are a few worthy of their time. There are seaside plantains, looking surprisingly like a large variety of the lawn nuisance of that name. In the autumn a purple *Gerardia* advertises its presence so it cannot be missed. Sea milkwort, a small, inconspicuous plant tucked away among the grasses, will take some looking for. In spite of its reputation for rarity, it probably occurs in most of the drier marshes of Cape Cod, as it does in Maine and Nova Scotia.

Much has been written about our salt marshes and their importance, but nothing more satisfying and more compelling than an article by Edward Weeks in *The Atlantic* of March, 1965. By the courtesy of Mr. Weeks and with the consent of *The Atlantic,* we reproduce his article, with two small omissions, here:

"As I look back it seems to me that all my life I have been in close touch with marshes — and always have I taken them for granted. As a child I could see from my nursery window the miles of marsh that separated my hometown from Jersey City: on an autumn evening the tall, dry cattails would catch fire from the sparks of the Pennsylvania locomotives and start a blaze that would sweep on for miles. Summers during my boyhood I lived on the Barnegat, which is to say, I lived half in the marsh and half in the sea. I cruised through the marshes from Bay Head to Cape May; I remember the snipe and the ducks which used to throng them in September just before I went back to school; I remember the odor of the marshland under the hot August sun, and when I catch a whiff of it today, a current of nostalgia flashes through me. In New England and especially since my fortieth year, when I became an angler, the marshes of Plum Island, of the Rowley and Ipswich rivers, the Essex marsh and the Nauset marsh on Cape Cod, sacred to the memory of Wyman Richardson, have held a special meaning. But my love for them has been unconcerned; not till five years ago did I realize that our salt marshes were in jeopardy and that we should have to fight to keep them alive — them and all the marine life that depends on them.

THE UPLAND FOREST

WHEN THE Pilgrims landed at Provincetown Harbor, most of Cape Cod was heavily forested; not the salt marshes, of course, and not the dunes, but probably all of what we are here calling upland. The Indians had cleared a little of it; Champlain in 1605 remarked on the corn they were growing on fields at the margin of the Eastham plains. A few samples of this original forest still remain — Lowell Reservation, in Sandwich and Mashpee, contains most of the upland forest species, including magnificent beeches and hollies.

As the Cape was settled, the land was cleared for agriculture by cutting and burning. Wood for fuel and lumber for houses and boats came from the forests that remained. White pine and white oak were of special value and soon largely disappeared. Other oaks, birches, beech, and hickory were burned for charcoal. Thoreau, writing of his stagecoach journey from Sandwich to Orleans in October, 1848, describes the results of all this cutting. "The country was, for the most part, bare, or with only a little scrubby wood left on the hills. We noticed in Yarmouth — and, if I do not mistake, in Dennis — large tracts where pitch pines were planted a few years before."

The Cape was probably never more bare of forest than at the time of Thoreau's visit. But the species left behind because of their low economic value were also species capable of re-establishing themselves under the most adverse conditions. They all produce abundant viable seeds, and almost all of them sprout from the roots after cutting or burning. The characteristic species are pitch pine, red and scarlet oak, and, near the shore, scrub oak. These and their less abundant associates, together with the shrubs and vines that grow under their cover and about their margins, make up our present upland forest.

An all too common vine of this habitat is poison ivy, *Rhus radicans*. It has an even more poisonous relative growing in many of our fresh-water swamps; this is poison sumac, *Rhus Vernix,* a tall shrub with shiny leaves that turn brilliant red in autumn and make trouble for occasional uninformed collectors of autumn foilage. Both these poisonous species have white or cream-colored fruits. Two other shrubby relatives, dwarf sumac and smooth sumac, sometimes grow together in dense thickets; they, along with all other species of *Rhus* with red fruits are not poisonous. Bearberry, called kinnekinnick in the Middle West, is not confined to the forest; it grows almost to the water's edge in some places, and covers the bare hills of Truro with a magnificent green carpet.

Beach plum and bayberry fill openings in the forest, and they, too, are not confined to the shore. In the spring the flowers of the shadbush make us aware of its abundance. Broom crowberry, *Corema Conradi,* is a specialty of the Cape. It occurs in dense clumps in open places in scattered localities from the Lowell Reservation in Mashpee to High Head in Truro. It looks like a heather and is often mistaken for one. It shows the discontinuous distribution that we expect of plants confined to special habitats, such as mountain tops, acid bogs, and the like, but the controlling factor is not clear in this case. It is found in the pine barrens of central New Jersey; in the Shawangunk Mountain ridge of eastern New York; on the Cape; in the western part of mainland Nova Scotia; on Prince Edward Island and the Magdalen Islands; and probably on Newfoundland.

For other plants of this habitat the illustrations should be consulted.

d as
their
bing
the
dian
hite
ible
ing
on
non-
ther
ytes.
un-
eria
ecay,
ring
ars,
ss of
into
hytic
hoto-
e on

living
grows
these
iving
sorbs
ead,

substances secreted by the fungus cause an abnormal enlargement and blackening of the plum or cherry twigs and stems. The result is the formation of the conspicuous black knots, often quite large, on our wild plums, on black cherry, and, less often, on beach plum. Another filamentous fungus, *Claviceps purpurea*, grows in the flowers of rye and a few other grasses. In the infected heads the ripening fruits are grain-shaped and greatly enlarged, and purplish or black in color. The disease is called ergot, and the enlarged grains are poisonous; before this was recognized, ergot poisoning often occurred in countries where rye bread was an important item of diet. On the Cape we sometimes find a great rarity, ergot in the heads of salt marsh grass, *Spartina alterniflora*.

The importance of the parasitic bacteria and fungi lies in their effects on their host plants. These range from the deformations in black knot on black cherry trees to the virtual extermination of our native chestnut trees in fifteen years by the fungus *Endothia parasitica*, accidentally introduced from China. Many other examples could be cited; these will serve to demonstrate the importance of the parasitic plants of the lower groups.

Much less important are the relatively few parasitic flowering plants. Dodder, *Cuscuta* sp., a yellowish vine twining about the stems of alfalfa and a dozen other kinds of herbaceous plants, sends its roots into the stems of its host plants and absorbs its food directly from them. Its flowers produce seeds with enough stored food to enable the seedling to grow to a few inches in height. If it comes in contact with a suitable host plant and establishes its connection, it lives; if it does not, it dies.

A third sort of relationship to food supply is displayed by the bacteria which enter and grow in the roots of leguminous plants such as clover. Secretions of the bacteria result in an enlargement of the infected roots and the formation of small nodules. The bacteria obtain their food from the roots of the host plants; that is, they are parasitic on the clover. But while growing in these living cells (but not outside in the soil, and not in culture solutions) they take nitrogen and hydrogen from the water of the cells and combine them to form ammonium compounds, which are used by the clover plant in its growth. This process of combining nitrogen with hydrogen and, later, other elements, is called nitrogen fixation and is of great benefit to the clover plant. It is the reason for the agricultural practice of growing leguminous crops in a rotation with other crops of greater immediate value, to increase the fertility of soils.

This relationship of mutual benefit to both plants is called symbiosis, and the partners in the arrangements are called symbionts. The lichens, especially abundant along seashores and in swamps because of the high humidity of the air in such habitats, are probably the most successful of all the practitioners of this symbiotic relationship.

MUSHROOMS AND PUFFBALLS

IN SPITE OF the apparent sterility of our sandy soil, mushrooms and puffballs are abundant in season in our woods and even in the valleys between fixed dunes. The mycelium thrives unseen on the organic material accumulated in the soil. After years of growth and food storage, a sporophore develops and thrusts itself to the surface almost overnight, sheds its spores, and dies. We are not surprised when a jonquil produces a flower, for we knew the bulb was there; but we may be surprised by the mushroom or puffball, for we have no way of knowing in advance where the mycelium is growing.

The spores of a mushroom are produced on the surfaces of flat gill-like plates on the lower side of the cap, or on the inner surfaces of short tubes, open at the lower ends, and similarly placed on the cap. The spores mature in a few hours and fall between the gills or out of the tubes into the open air, to be carried away by the wind. If a cap with ripening spores is placed, flat side down, on a piece of white paper and covered with a tumbler or dish, the spores falling on the paper will stick to it and the "spore print" resulting will accurately represent the number, size, and shape of the gills or pores.

The spores of a puffball are produced in closed cavities within the sporophore, and ripen there. When they are mature, the sporophore dies and dries out, one or more openings in its outer wall forming at this time. The mycelium contained in the sporophore, including that forming the walls of the cavities containing the spores, all becomes very brittle, breaking up under the least force applied to it, and so releasing the spores. When this has happened, anything striking the outside of the puffball, even a drop of rain, will puff the spores out, to be distributed by the wind.

There are many genera and species of mushrooms and puffballs along our shores and on the sand hills, and only a few of them can be illustrated. *Laccaria trullisata* produces its spores on gills which are relatively few in number and exceptionally thick. *Boletus* is an important genus of the pore mushrooms; in one common species the underside of the cap, where the pores can be seen, is at first yellow, but turns brown with time. One species of *Lycoperdon*, a common puffball, grows to a diameter of six or eight inches. In this genus the wall of the sporophore is thin and the ripe spores escape when the wall ruptures.

Perhaps the most interesting of the puffballs, and in most parts of the Cape the commonest, is the earth star, *Geaster hygrometricus*. When the spores are maturing inside it the sporophore is a flattened spheroid an inch or a little more in diameter, and a little less than that in height. The wall enclosing the spores is double; the outer wall, called the peridium, is much thicker than the inner. At maturity, the peridium splits radially into 6 or 8 arms, which then bend back until they are flat against the ground. The thin inner wall does not split, but develops a small opening or pore at its upper center. The star-shaped peridium, with the spherical container of the spores at its center, fully justifies the common name of this fungus.

In the opened condition any object falling on the central sphere will puff spores out through the pore. As the sporophore dries, the arms curve up again, finally enclosing the central sphere again. In wet weather the arms open out again, often curving back against the ground with enough force to break the mycelial threads that connect it with the mycelium in the ground. In the next dry period, with the arms wrapped tightly about the central sphere, it may roll or blow along the ground, distributing spores as it goes.

Only a few of the mushrooms and puffballs of the shore can be illustrated. For any extensive program of identification, some authoritative handbook or manual should be employed. Even with these, you will not find a description of a pore mushroom of which specimens were found on Monomoy Point, south of Chatham, in the autumn of 1956. Mr. Walter Shea, of the Boston Mycological Club, has very kindly furnished an account of the structure of the specimen and of its identification.

A specimen was collected by a small group which included Mr. and Mrs. Edward Norman. Mrs. Norman made a water color study of the specimen, and sent both the specimen and the drawing to Mr. Shea. The drawing arrived in good condition, and is now in the collection of the Boston Mycological Club, but the specimen was described as "smelling of rotten fish and broken beyond preservation." From the drawing, the broken specimen, and the description sent by the party, it was possible to

Each spring we seem to see this "invention" of chlorophyll happen all over again. Growth occurs, new twigs or new plants bear new leaves, and, above all, new chlorophyll is formed; this is the significance of spring. Here it happens suddenly, for spring is the shortest of our seasons; according to some grumblers, it is sometimes only a date. Higher sun, longer days, and rising temperatures combine to accelerate not only photosynthesis but all the many processes that constitute plant growth.

Summer is at first only a continuation of spring, but soon new factors come to bear. With higher temperatures, increased evaporation from twigs and leaves checks growth, wilts plants, and kills some of them. During the New England drought of 1964-1966 dead trees appeared in increasing numbers in our forests. During the summer photosynthesis proceeds steadily at a rate controlled by such factors as light intensity and temperature, but the utilization of its all-important product, sugar, undergoes an important change. Leaf formation and growth in length of twigs stops first, then growth in diameter of trunks and of twigs stops. Food storage in roots and stems begins, and increases as growth slows. By late August all growth has stopped and only food storage is going on. With the arrival of autumn our trees and shrubs have made their season's growth and have completed their preparation, not only for the dormancy of winter but also for all the activity of next spring.

The evergreen conifers make no autumn adjustment to the conditions of winter. They are evergreen because their leaves are not killed by winter and live more than one season, three seasons in the case of pitch pine. They have a definite period of leaf fall, late summer and early autumn in most cases. Because of low temperatures very little photosynthesis goes on in the winter, but it begins early in the spring, since there is no waiting for new leaves to appear. Since the conifers do not "shorten sail" in the autumn, some are blown over by winter storms, and a few are killed by drying out when the trunks are frozen and no water can be brought up from the roots.

As for our deciduous trees, the arrival of autumn means the beginning of that carnival of color that is without equal outside New England. With the gradual disappearance of the chlorophyll the associated yellow pigments in the leaves are revealed; and here they rival the effects that the same pigments produce in yellow flowers, and surpass their best effects in the coloring of the lowly carrot. Then the red appears, new to tree leaves but not to all leaves. This is the red pigment in *Begonia* and *Coleus* leaves, the red pigment in the leaves and swollen root of red beet. Its formation is favored by low temperature — anything below 40°Fahr. is as effective as frost — and by sunshine. This is why we can predict a magnificent display of red in an autumn of bright, cool days, and only a poor display in one of warm and cloudy weather.

The last of the series of colors in every case is brown. This follows death of the cells of the leaf and is the result of an initial oxidation of the cell wall material, a beginning of the processes of decay. In elm it follows the display of yellow and the fall of the leaves; you see yellow leaves on the trees, brown ones on the ground beneath. In maples and sumacs the sequence is a brief yellow period, then red, then brown.

Leaf fall completes the series of events in most cases. A layer of cork forms across the base of the leaf-stalk, cutting off the water supply of the leaf and at the same time introducing a weak element into a previously strong structure. After it is formed, a puff of wind, or even the weight of a layer of frost is enough to bring the leaf down. The conifers do not "shorten sail" for the winter, but the deciduous trees go in "under bare poles."

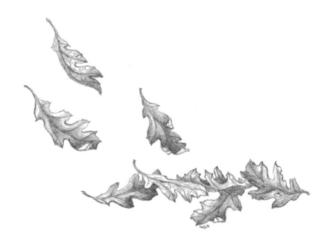

ON THE WAY TO THE BEACH

M G N ×½ approx.

Bouncing-Bet or Soapwort
(Saponaria officinalis)

A sturdy perennial.
Flowers - pale pink to cream
July ~ September

Shadbush
(Amelanchier canadensis)

A shrub with several trunks and generally
   upright branches.
Young leaves - fuzzy on the back, becoming
   smooth upon maturing.
Flowers :- April ~ early June ~ white

Scotch Broom
(cytisus scoparius)

Shrub with stiff, green
ribbed branches
Leaflets small and in 3s.
Bright yellow flowers
May ~ June

Scarlet Pimpernel, Poor-Man's-weather-glass
(Anagallis arvensis)

A low, sprawling plant.
Flowers: close in cloudy weather, as name shows
scarlet with minute hairs like fringe
on the petals. Variable in size.
Leaves: with black dots (glandular) on the back
← seed
capsule   Flowers May ~ early fall.

Chicory
or
Blue Sailors
(Cichorium Intybus)

Flowers: bright
blue
July ~ October

Opening only in sun.

Common Evening Primrose
(Oenothera biennis)

Flowers - yellow
opening toward
evening

June ~ October

MGN

X ½ approx.

Queen Anne's Lace
(Daucus Carota)

A biennial

Flowers - whitish or
rosy (less common)

May ~ October

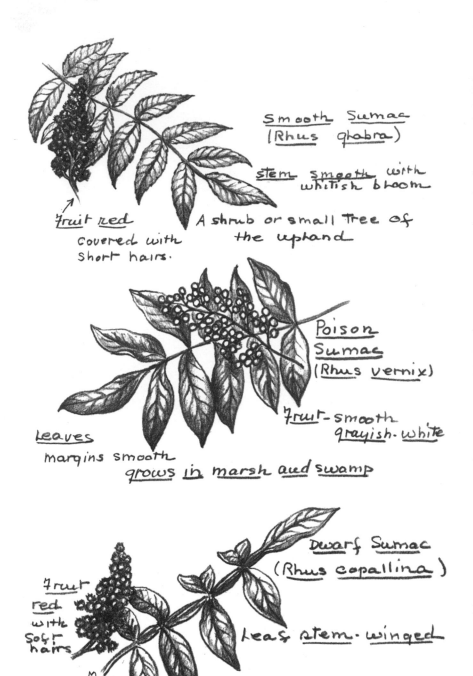

Smooth Sumac
(Rhus glabra)

stem smooth with
whitish bloom

Fruit red
covered with
short hairs.

A shrub or small tree of
the upland

Poison
Sumac
(Rhus vernix)

Fruit - smooth
grayish-white

Leaves
margins smooth
grows in marsh and swamp

Dwarf Sumac
(Rhus copallina)

Fruit
red
with
soft
hairs

Leaf stem-winged

Smooth Sumac
Rhus glabra

A smooth shrub with whitish bloom (glaucous) on stems. the fleshy fruit (drupe) covered with fine hairs.
June ~ July
Grows at back of marsh, Toward the upland.

AT THE TIDE LINE

Eel grass
(Zostera marina)
grows in shallow water
Flowers hidden in leaf sheaths.
Not a true grass
but a member of the
Pondweed family - Zosteraceae

Sea Lettuce
(Ulva Lactuca)
Green Algae

Tissue-thin; bright, light green

Enteromorpha intestinalis
green seaweed

Blade: tubular, growing singly or in
colonies.

Holdfast: tiny disk, attaching to stones, wood,
or shells in the intertidal zone.

Codium fragile
green seaweed

An erect, dark green plant.
Branches, always dividing in twos,
        covered with fine filaments
        giving a velvety texture.
Holdfast: attached to shells; oysters,
        scallops or small stones.

65

Rockweed
Fucus vesiculosis
Brown seaweed

Fronds: flat, leathery, with pairs of oval air
vessels, one on each side of the
prominent mid-rib. Forked
branching usually in twos.
Holdfast: attached to stones, rocks or
wharf pilings. This seaweed is
usually exposed at low tide.

66

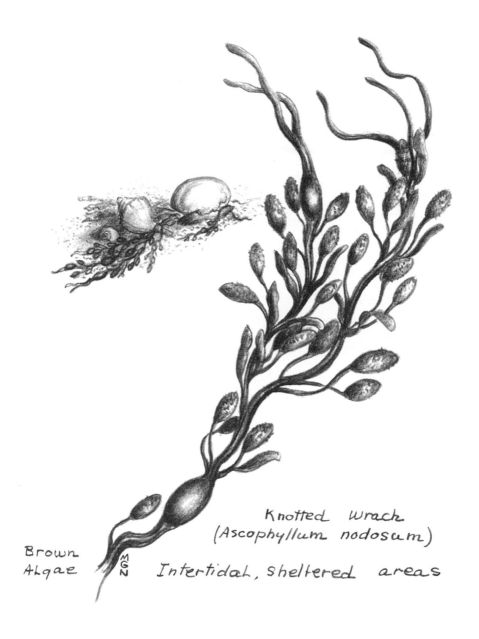

Knotted Wrack
(Ascophyllum nodosum)

Brown
Algae

MGN

Intertidal, sheltered areas

67

Sargassum
(Sargassum filipendula)
Brown Algae

the common attached Sargassum of
the Atlantic. the air bladders (vesicles)
growing from the attachments of the
Leaf-Like blades.

Kelp
Laminaria agardhii
Brown algae

The most common of the kelps,
growing in mussel beds, and
attached to pilings.

Holdfast is finger-like.

Winged Kelp
(Alaria esculenta)
Brown Seaweed (Algae)
of great size.

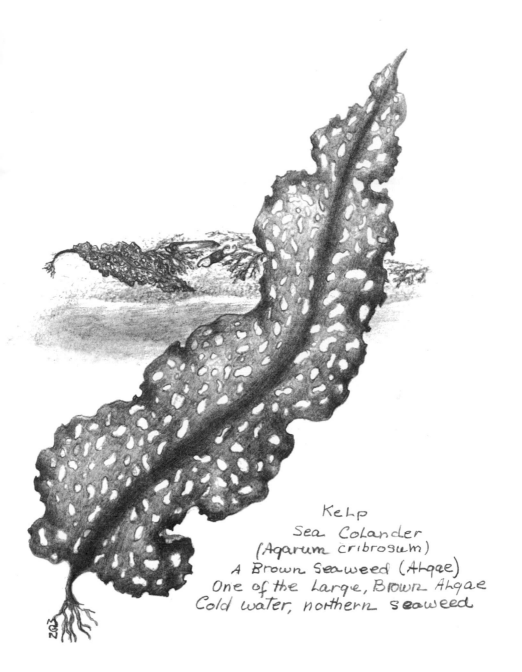

Kelp
Sea Colander
(Agarum cribrosum)
A Brown Seaweed (Algae)
One of the Large, Brown Algae
Cold water, northern seaweed

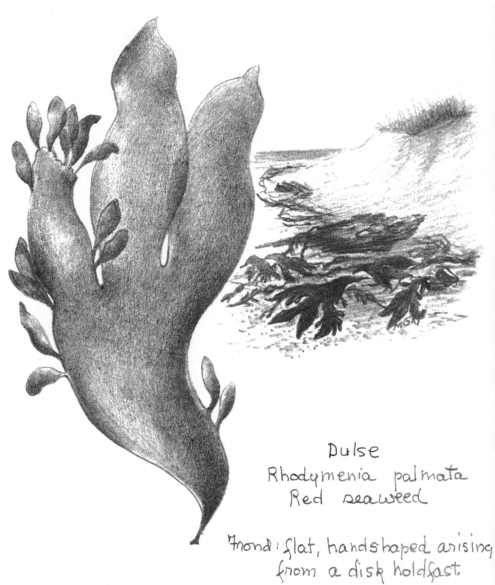

Dulse
Rhodymenia palmata
Red seaweed

Frond: flat, handshaped arising
from a disk holdfast.
Leaflets often growing from margin of blade.
Plants sizeable, usually deep red.
Intertidal zone into deep water.

Irish   Moss
(Chondrus crispus)
Red Algae
A seaweed of the low tide line
growing in dense clumps.
Deep purple or purple-green

BACK ON THE DUNES

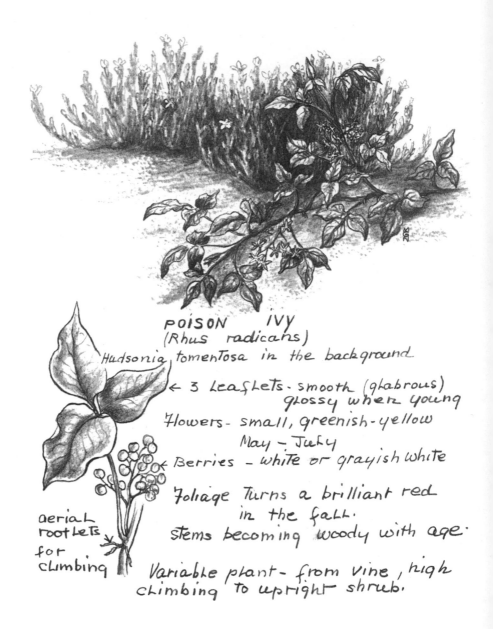

POISON IVY
(Rhus radicans)
Hudsonia tomentosa in the background

← 3 Leaflets - smooth (glabrous)
          glossy when young
Flowers - small, greenish-yellow
        May - July
← Berries - white or grayish white

Foliage turns a brilliant red
      in the fall.
Stems becoming woody with age.

aerial
rootlets
for
climbing

Variable plant - from vine, high
climbing to upright shrub.

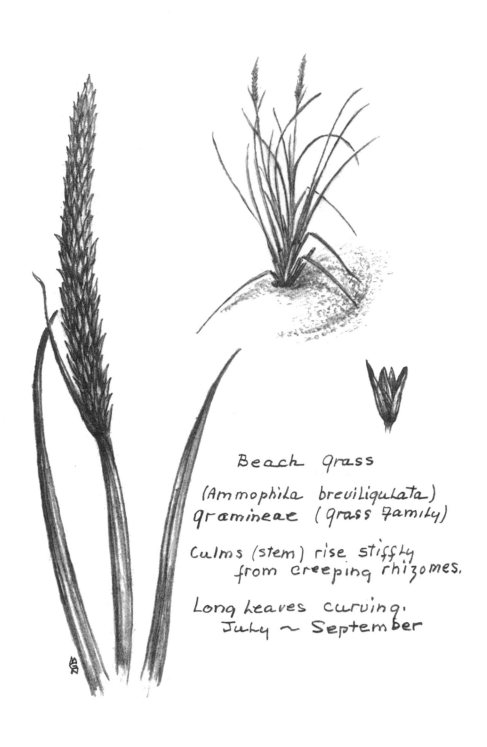

Beach grass

(Ammophila breviligulata)
gramineae (grass family)

Culms (stem) rise stiffly
    from creeping rhizomes.

Long leaves curving.
    July ~ September

disk flowers

Wormwood
(Artemisia caudata)

This plant is usually biennial.
Leaves: pinnately divided, the segments
     linear.
Flowers: small, greenish-yellow.
     Flower stalks arise from the
first year's growth.
          July and August.

Flower

Flowers – yellow
July – September

Leaves pale green
covered with
white woolly hairs

Dusty Miller
Artemisia Stelleriana

Beach Pea
Lathyrus japonicus var. glaber
Flowers in clusters (racemes)
violet — purple
Blossoms throughout summer

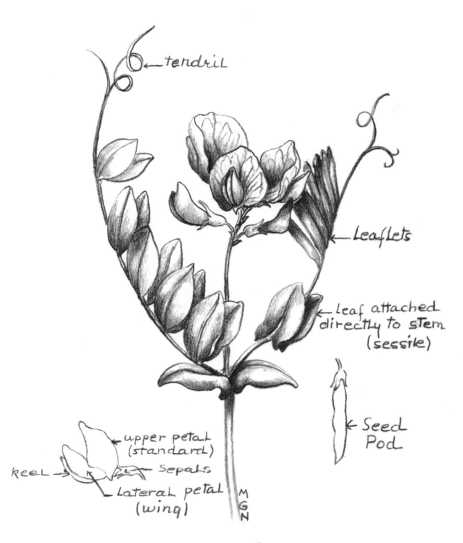

tendril

Leaflets

leaf attached directly to stem (sessile)

Seed Pod

upper petal (standard)

keel

sepals

Lateral petal (wing)

MGN

Beach Pea

Flowers in clusters (racemes)
Color:- blue~violet
blossoming throughout summer

81

Salt-Spray Rose   (Rosa rugosa)
    Dense shrub-like growth
Leaflets: 5-9 on stem - dark green
        margin toothed-curving back
Flowers- purplish-rose or white
      through summer to frost
Fruit (Hip): smooth and red

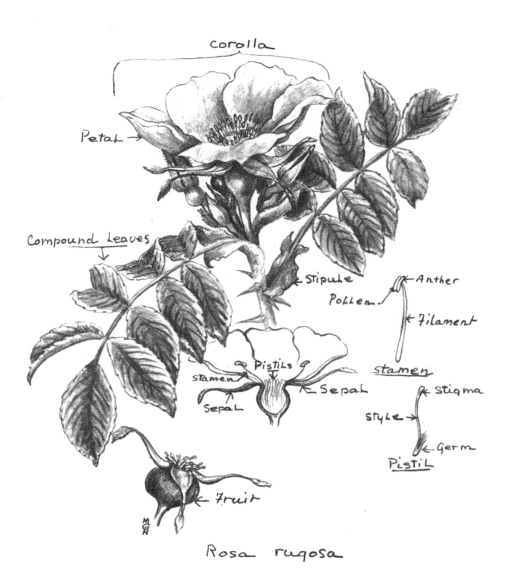

corolla

Petal →

Compound Leaves

Stipule

Anther

Pollen.

Filament

stamen

Pistils

stamen →

Sepal → Sepal

Sepal

Stigma

Style →

Germ

Pistil

Fruit

M
G
R

Rosa rugosa

Fruit

Rosa virginiana

Flowers: pink.   thorns: recurving
Fruit: Bristly, glandular or smooth.
Late June ~ August
Damp thickets and shores.

Seaside Spurge
Euphorbia polygonifolia

Plant prostrate, grows flat on sand.
Flowers: tiny, green, seeds larger.
Leaves: oblong-lanceolate
Stems: green becoming red
July ~ October

Dusty Miller
in background

Common Saltwort
(Barilla-plant)

(Salsola Kali)

A bushy, annual plant

Flowers — whitish at leaf axils
Leaves — stiff with barb at tip.
July ~ October

Seabeach Orach
(Atriplex arenaria)

↑ Fruit
detail

A branching, annual plant.

Leaves: grey-green, scurfy (mealy)

Stem: tinged with red, dotted with
whitish granules toward base.

Flowers: greenish, minute
July ~ September.

Fruit: winged and distinctive

87

Sea Rocket
cakile edentula

Pale Lavender blossoms
July ~ September

Rocket-shaped seed capsule ---->
Leaves- slightly toothed (dentate)

Seabeach Sandwort
(Arenaria peploides)
Flowers: small, few at leaf axils.
June ~ August
Leaves: fleshy
A succulent, procumbent beach
plant, forming large carpets over
the sand.

seed

Sickle-Leaved Golden Aster
(Chrysopsis falcata)

Leaves - narrow, curved
   Stem - white, woolly hairs when young
Blossoms - golden yellow

         July ~ September

   grows in sandy, dry areas

Poverty grass
or
Beach Heath
(Hudsonia tomentosa)

—detail

A low shrubby plant

Leaves- scale-like, close to stem, downy.

Flowers- bright yellow, open in sun.
May through July

Hudsonia ericoides is less
common. Very similar to
Hudsonia tomentosa, but with
spreading leaves, not clinging
to the stem.

← detail

Hudsonia ericoides

Cocklebur
(Xanthium echinatum)
Sea Rocket in background.

Detail of
bur.

Coarse, annual plant.
Leaves: somewhat cordate,
    heart-shaped, with undulate margins.
Stems: mottled purple.
Flowers: inconspicuous
Burs: conspicuous, with hooked prickles
    which have stiff hairs at the base

Late August ~ October

Seaside Goldenrod

Solidago sempervirens

Leaves - thick, sessile (attached to stem)

Flower - golden yellow

August to fall frost

Jointweed
Polygonella articulata

Stem: wiry, jointed, branched, with a whitish
        covering.
Leaves: Linear inconspicuous and deciduous.
Flowers: white or rose, growing in slender raceme
                July ~ October

94

Pinweed
Lechea maritima
perennial herb

Stem: erect or inclined, rigid, hairy toward base.
Leaves: elliptical, up to $\frac{1}{2}$ inch long.
Flowers: Tiny, red- purple.
    Basal shoots growing in a rosette
   with thick, lanceolate, hoary, leaves.
     August to frost

Juncus Greenei
Rush family
Hudsonia in background

detail

Leaves: involute, i.e. rolled in, growing
about the base of the plant.
Distinguishing feature: sepals are
shorter than the seed capsule.
Note the detail.
Growing on sand dunes and other sandy areas.
June ~ September

Bearberry
(Arctostaphylos Uva-ursi)

.A creeping, prostrate, evergreen shrub.
Forms a ground cover
over sandy soil.

Calyx
pink

Fruit
red

Flowers white or white with pink tips.
May through June

Bayberry (myrica pensylvanica)
Leaves — slightly toothed toward tip
Forms clusters of round nuts
covered with grayish-white wax.
    Bayberry is a shrub which is
mostly dioecious.

Beach Plum   Fruit
Prunus maritima

A low, sprawling shrub.
Branches: red-brown with tan dots
    on the bark.
Blossoms: snowy white, becoming pinkish
    with age.
    Late April ~ early June.
Fruit: varying in color, reddish purple to blue
    purple.
    September ~ October.

Pitch Pine
(Pinus rigida)

Leaves (needles) in 3s

Each scale of the cone
has a sharp, recurved
barb or prickle.

Scrub Oak
(Quercus ilicifolia)

Black Oak Group
straggling shrub or small Tree
Acorns - small - approximately ½ inch
       high; saucer-shaped cup.
grows far back on the sand dunes
and in barren, upland soil.

Broom Crowberry
(Corema Conradii)
Lichen beneath in the foreground

A small, shrubby, plant.
  Leaves: needle-like, evergreen
      and tiny.
  Flowers: at tip of branches.
anther
brown-
purple
  Fruit: tiny-nut-like berry.
  Flowering: early April ~ May.
filament-purple, making the flower showy

Red Crest Lichen
or
British Soldiers
(Cladonia cristatella)
Stalk - greenish - grey
Fruit (cap) - bright red.

Thorn Lichen
(Cladonia uncialis)
yellowish - green
stalks branching
grows clumps.
when dry, rigid, sharp spiny.

slender
Reindeer Moss
(Cladonia tenuis)
Pale greenish - grey
Tips - slender, drooping
forms large mats.
Similar species: (Cladonia rangiferina)
Larger - silver grey - less common

Alpine
Reindeer Moss
(Cladonia alpestris)
forms domes
Pale creamy grey

Iceland Moss
(Cetraria islandica)
Brown - forking stalks
curl when dry.
Grows in tufty, tangled masses.

the   Sod   Lichen
growing on the sand, far back
on the protected areas of the dunes.

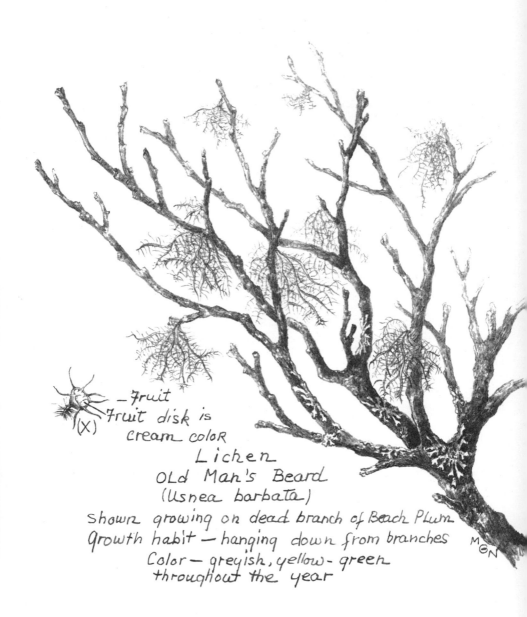

—Fruit
Fruit disk is
cream coloR

(X)

Lichen
OLd Man's Beard
(Usnea barbata)
shown growing on dead branch of Beach Plum
Growth habit — hanging down from branches
Color — greyish, yellow-green
throughout the year

M©N

Mushroom   Development

— spore or single cell in soil

— cell growth to form single thread or hypha

— mass of Threads = mycelium

— mycelium threads grown together to form tiny ball which develops into mushroom!

— tiny mushroom buttons on the mycelium A mass of mycelium threads must develop to produce a few mushrooms.

Types of structure of mushroom gills

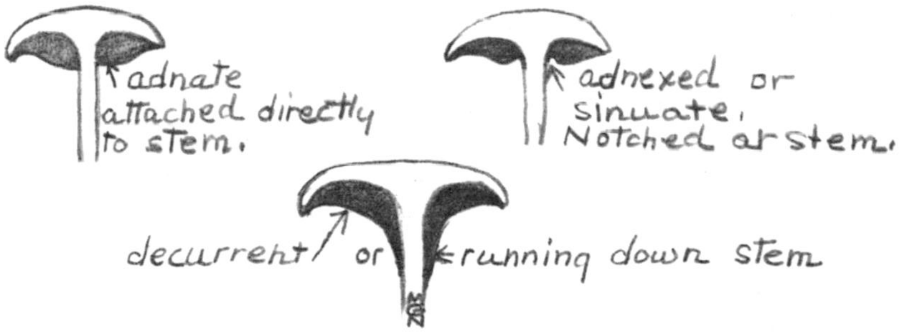

adnate attached directly to stem.

adnexed or sinuate. Notched at stem.

decurrent or running down stem

Sandy Laccaria
(Laccaria trullisata)
Late summer through fall.
Cap - Reddish Tan - thin, becomes
    depressed in center with age
gills - purple violet becoming brick red
    unequal, thick, adnate, some with
    decurrent tooth
Stem - color of cap, sand clings to base.
Hudsonia tomentosa in the background.

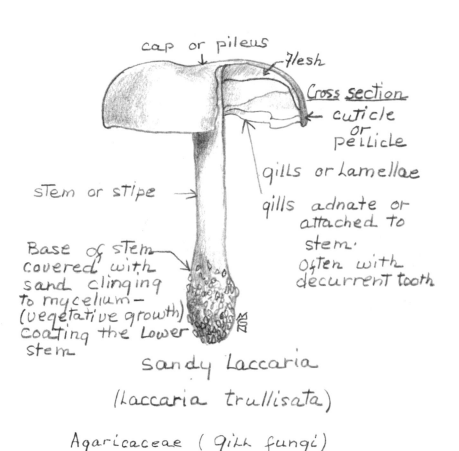

cap or pileus

flesh

Cross <u>section</u>

cuticle
or
pellicle

gills or Lamellae

gills adnate or
attached to
stem.
Often with
decurrent tooth

stem or stipe

Base of stem
covered with
sand clinging
to mycelium —
(vegetative growth)
coating the Lower
stem

Sandy Laccaria

(Laccaria trullisata)

Agaricaceae (gill fungi)

Boletus scaber
Stem - with brown rough dots at Top
Color of cap very variable from
yellowish tan to red brown.
Mid-summer through autumn

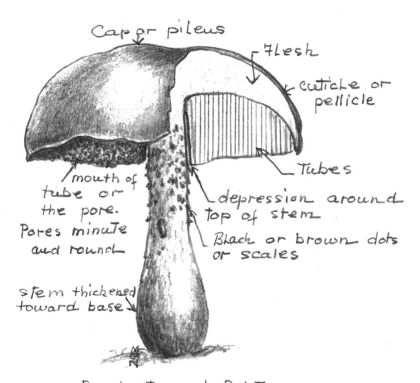

Cap or pileus

Flesh

cuticle or pellicle

Tubes

depression around top of stem

Black or brown dots or scales

mouth of tube or the pore. Pores minute and round

stem thickened toward base

Rough-stemmed Boletus
(Boletus Scaber)
Polyporaceae (Pore or tube fungi)

Cap: 1 to 5 inches broad

grows in sandy soil

Earth - Star
(Geaster hygrometricus)
with Cladonia Lichen in background

Puff-ball-like top, greyish cream color

Star-like appendages - dark brown
Late summer ~ Fall

Earth - Star
(geaster hygrometricus)

Lycoperdaceae - (Pouch fungi)

Outer coating (Peridium) cracks to form
star-like appendages, which curl in dry
weather to form a ball which rolls about
releasing the spores from the opening
in the Top of the pouch. In wet weather
the star-like points cling to the ground
by the gelatinous undercoating, prevent-
ing the loss of the spores (seeds) in
bad weather

THE SALT MARSH

Salt. Marsh Grass
Spartina alterniflora

Spikelets: alternating.
Leaves: flat and tough.
Growing in salt marshes along
the creeks, the lower part
covered at high tide.

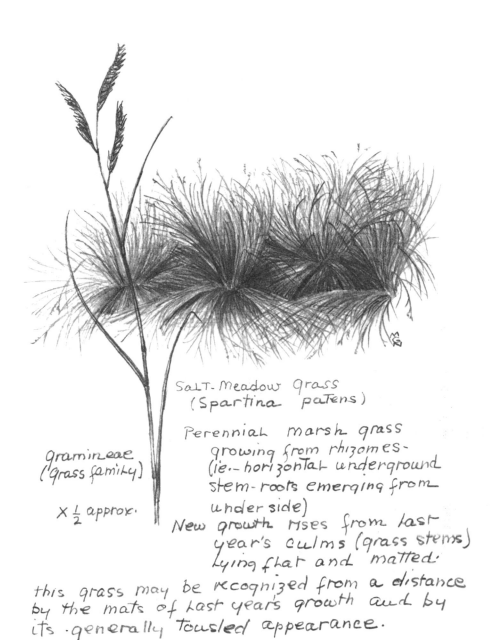

Salt-Meadow Grass
(Spartina patens)

gramineae
('grass family)

X ½ approx.

Perennial marsh grass
growing from rhizomes.
(ie.- horizontal underground
stem-roots emerging from
under side)
New growth rises from last
year's culms (grass stems)
lying flat and matted.
this grass may be recognized from a distance
by the mats of last year's growth and by
its generally tousled appearance.

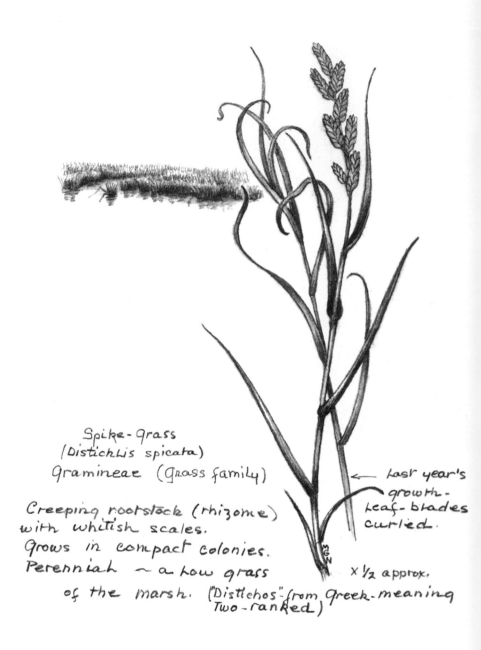

Spike-grass
(Distichlis spicata)
Gramineae (grass family)

← Last year's
growth.
Leaf-blades
curled.

Creeping rootstock (rhizome)
with whitish scales.
Grows in compact colonies.
Perennial ~ a low grass
   of the marsh. ("Distichos"-from Greek-meaning
     Two-ranked)

x ½ approx.

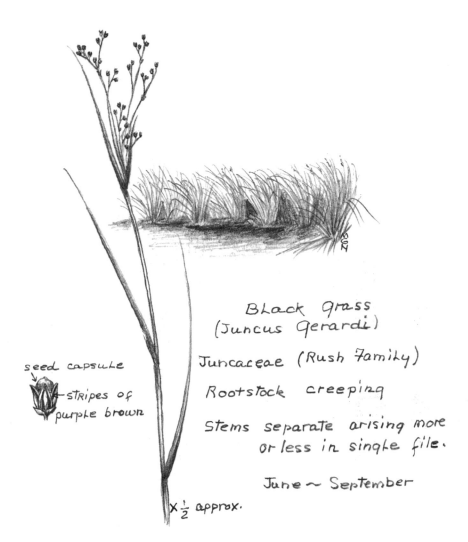

seed capsule

stripes of purple brown

Black grass
(Juncus Gerardi)

Juncaceae (Rush Family)

Rootstock creeping

Stems separate arising more
or less in single file.

June ~ September

X ½ approx.

117

Sedge
(Cyperus polystachyos)
var. texensis

Cyperaceae (Sedge Family)

Spikelets — yellowish to
rust color

Late July ~ October

← X ½ approx.

seed detail

Halberd-leaved Orach
Atriplex patula var. hastata

Stem: smooth, green or reddish, angled,
    slightly granular.
Leaves: triangular
Flowers: tiny, green
    August ~ October

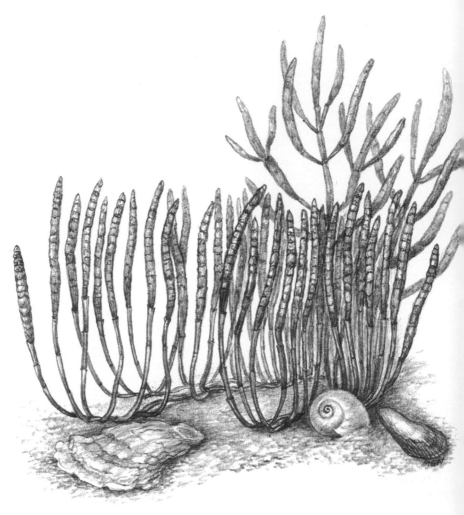

Woody Glasswort
(Salicornia virginica)

A perennial, marsh plant, forming
sizable mats. Grows from, a woody,
creeping, main stem. Roots at nodes.

Flowers: Embedded in hollows of the
upper joints of the spike.
　　Green, turning dull grey in fall.
　　August ～ October

Salicornia europaea in background.

120

Samphire or Glasswort

Annuals: branched, succulent, jointed stems.
Flowers: tiny, in hollows of upper joints.
Plant green turning orange to red in fall.
Blossoms August~November

Salicornia Bigelovii (above)
middle flower higher.
Pointed margins of scales.
Joints thicker than long.

Salicornia europaea (above)
joints longer than thick.

Considerably taller than
Salicornia Bigelovii

121

Early Seaside Plantain
Plantago juncoides var. decipiens

Leaves: fleshy, narrow, linear. Flowers: pale, off-white.
A deep-rooted perennial of the marsh.
June ~ Early August

Late Seaside Plantain
Plantago oliganthos

Leaves: erect, Linear, triangular
in cross-section.
Flowers: small, whitish.
July ~ September

Leaf
flat on top

Sea - BLite
(Suaeda maritima)

-7lower
pale green

Marsh Samphire in the background
1-4 7lowers at Leaf axils
Stem tinged with red
July — October

seed detail

Coast Blite
Chenopodium rubrum

Stem: angular and branching.
Flowers: small, red, growing in clusters,
    turning a brilliant red in the fall.
    August to frost.

Sand Spurrey
Spergularia marina

Stem: prostrate or ascending.
Leaves: fleshy, linear.
flowers: pink.
    June ~ September

Sea Lavender ~ Marsh Rosemary
(Limonium carolinianum)
Samphire and Marsh grass in background
Flowers ~ Lavender or Light purple
July ~ October

127

Salt Marsh Fleabane
Pluchea purpurascens var. succulenta
Spartina patens in the background

Leaves: thick and toothed   Stem: thick
Flowers: Pink or purple in flat-topped clusters
August ～ September

Slender-leaved Goldenrod
Solidago tenuifolia

stem: slender, wiry, slightly
    angled
Leaves: thin and narrow.
Flowers: golden yellow.
    July ~ October

Salt-Marsh Aster
(perennial)
(Aster tenuifolius)

Stem smooth
Leaves Linear

Flowers:- Late August
through October
pale Lavender
or
whitish

stems generally zigzag.

Silverweed

Potentilla anserina

Plant grows from runners.

Leaves: sharply toothed, deep green above, whitish below.

Flowers: bright yellow.   June ~ August.

Seaside Gerardia
(Gerardia maritima)

Stems may be simple (as shown) or branched
Leaves and stem: green, purple tinged.
Flowers:- pink to rose purple
July ~ September

Blue-eyed grass
(Sisyrinchium arenicola,
stems erect, flattened
leaves light green

Spathe (bract enclosing
  flowering head) is tinged
  with purple.
Flowers - blue-violet
    May ~ July

Yellow star in
center of
blossom

Ladies' Tresses
(Spiranthes cernua)

Marsh orchid with spiral
    flower stalk
Leaves – Light, yellow-green
Flowers – creamy-white
    August through September

X ½

MGN

Seabeach Knotweed
(Polygonum glaucum)

Plant more or less prostrate (flat)
    on the sand. grows in dune
hollows and brackish areas.

Flowers whitish or pink
    July ~ November

New stems,
silvery with
whitish hairs

old stem-
woody and

chestnut color

Sea Milkwort
(Glaux maritima)

A low, leafy perennial of marsh
and brackish areas.
  Leaves: opposite, sessile (without stems)
Flowers: white, lavender, or pink in
            leaf axils.
        Campanulate (bell shaped)
        June ~ July

Marsh Elder
Iva frutescens var. oraria

Perennial shrub

Leaves: Lanceolate, sharply
    toothed.
Flowers: on spikes arising
    from leaf axils.
    Greenish-white
August ~ October

137

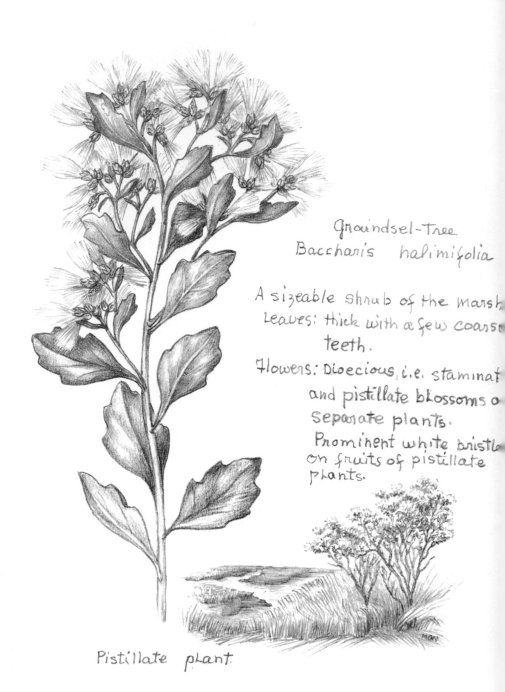

Groundsel-Tree
Baccharis halimifolia

A sizeable shrub of the marsh
Leaves: thick with a few coarse
teeth.
Flowers: Dioecious, i.e. staminate
and pistillate blossoms o
separate plants.
Prominent white bristle
on fruits of pistillate
plants.

Pistillate plant.

Late August ~ October

Groundsel — Tree
Baccharis halimifolia
Staminate plant

A dioecious shrub, i.e., pistillate and staminate
blossoms on separate plants, growing on the
borders of marshes.
Flowers: whitish or yellow.
Late August ~ October

139

Reed
(Phragmites communis)

grows in large colonies

Tall perennial grass

gramineae (grass family)

140

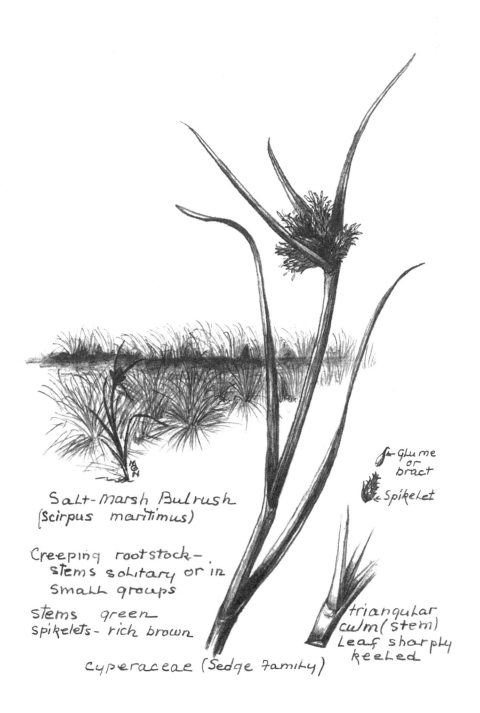

Salt-Marsh Bulrush
(Scirpus maritimus)

Creeping rootstock-
   stems solitary or in
   small groups

stems green
spikelets- rich brown

Cyperaceae (Sedge family)

Glume
or
bract

Spikelet

triangular
culm (stem)
Leaf sharply
keeled

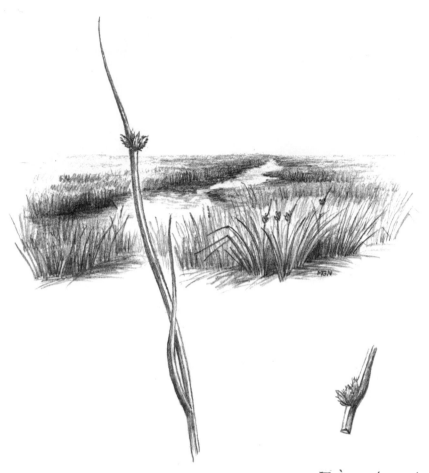

Triangular stem

Chair-maker's Rush
Scirpus americanus
Sedge Family

Spikelets: brown
Plant grows from an elongate rhizome
Smaller than Scirpus maritimus.
Brackish shores.
June ~ September

Soft Rush
Juncus effusus var. solutus

Inflorescence: loose and branched.

Marshes and brackish meadows.
July~ September

Sepals
longer than
petals

143

Scirpus atrovirens
Sedge family

Inflorescence: open.

Leaves: showing horizontal
ridges (septate) which
are very prominent
when dry.
Late June ~ August

144

Seaside Wild Rye
Elymus virginicus var. halophilu
grass family

Spikelets: pale
Leaves: generally involute,
          i.e. rolled in.

Growing in tussocks in brackish areas.
          Late July ~ October
Cat-tails in background require less saline
          water **than the** Elymus.

Panic Grass
(Panicum Longifolium)

Gramineae (Grass Family)

A perennial grass growing
in tufts.
July ~ October

←x½ approx.

146

Horned Rush
Rhynchospora macrostachya
Sedge family

Spikelets: 10-30 growing in clusters.
　　　Reddish-brown.
Bristles far exceeding the achenes,
　　　which are 1-seeded hard
　　　fruit.
　　　　　Late July~October
Background Cat-tails require less saline water.

Cat-tail
Typha Latifolia

Late May — July
No gap between pistillate and
staminate portions of the spike.
Grows at the back of the marsh
where some fresh water is
present.

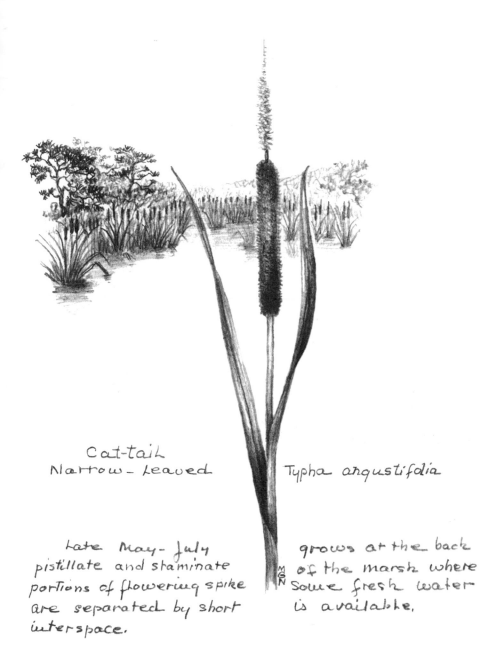

Cat-tail
Narrow-Leaved   Typha angustifolia

Late May-July
pistillate and staminate
portions of flowering spike
are separated by short
interspace.

grows at the back
of the marsh where
some fresh water
is available.

Salt Reed-grass
Spartina cynosuroides

Leaves: flat, rough below
and on margins.
Spikes: flowers in open raceme,
on an elongated axis; angled
upward from the stem.
Brown to purple. August~October.
A tall grass of brackish, marsh areas above
the high tide line.

Fresh Water Cord-Grass
Spartina pectinata

Leaves: tapering to slender points,
rough on the margins,
rolling inward on drying.
July ~ September
A tall grass growing in fresh
water marshes to brackish areas.

Scirpus cyperinus
Sedge family
Inflorescence: open   Leaves: linear, curving
Growing in dense clumps.
August ~ October

RECOMMENDED BOOKS AND REFERENCES

The following books, arranged in the order of their first publication, give descriptions of various aspects of the North Atlantic shore:

HENRY D. THOREAU, *Cape Cod.* The edition by Norton, 1951, includes a description of his fourth trip to the Cape, in 1857. On this trip he visited the south side of the Cape, from South Yarmouth to Harwich Port.

HENRY BESTON, *The Outermost House.* Viking, 1962, paperback.

WYMAN RICHARDSON, *The House on Nauset Marsh.* Norton, 1947.

JOHN HAY, *The Great Beach.* Doubleday, 1963.

GERALD WARNER BRACE, *Between Wind and Water.* Norton, 1966.

CHARLTON OGBURN, *The Winter Beach.* Morrow, 1966.

DOROTHY STERLING, *The Outer Lands.* Natural History Press, 1966.

JOHN HAY and PETER FARB, *The Atlantic Shore.* Harper and Row, 1966.

JOHN HAY, *The Sandy Shore.* Chatham Press, 1968.

Another comprehensive and authoritative manual of the vascular plants of northeastern North America is:

N. L. BRITTON and A. BROWN, *Illustrated Flora of the Northern United States,* edited by HENRY A. GLEASON. Three volumes, 1732 pages. Hafner Publishing Co., publisher for the New York Botanical Garden, 1963.

For a technical account of the development of a typical New England salt marsh, see:

ALFRED C. REDFIELD, "Ontogeny of a Salt Marsh Estuary." *"Science,* Vol. 147. No. 3653, pp. 50-55. January 1, 1965.

For general botanical information:

VICTOR A. GREULACH and J. EDISON ADAMS, *Plants: An Introduction to Modern Botany.* John Wiley and Sons, 1967.

HAROLD C. BOLD, *Morphology of Plants.* Harper and Row, 1967. This book is primarily concerned with plant structure as the basis for classification throughout the plant kingdom.

Two popular wild flower handbooks are:

LAWRENCE NEWCOMB, *Pocket Key to Common Wild Flowers.* New England Wild Flower Preservation Society, Boston, 1963.

HAROLD R. HINDS and WILFRED A. HATHAWAY, *Wildflowers of Cape Cod.* Chatham Press, 1968.

For the identification of plants of some of the lower groups, the following will be useful:

WILLIAM STURGIS THOMAS, *Field Book of Common Mushrooms,* Putnams, 1948.

LOUIS C. C. KRIEGER, *The Mushroom Handbook.* Dover Press, 1967.

MASON E. HALE, JR., *Lichen Handbook.* Smithsonian Institution, 1961.

INDEX